The Complete Dash Diet Plan

An Innovative Diet Plan Full of Delicious Recipes

Eleonore Barlow

TABLE OF CONTENTS

Poached Eggs with Hollandaise and Bacon

With this slimmed-down hollandaise, it is easy to enjoy a version of eggs Benedict that is SmartPoints-friendly. The sauce also makes an excellent combination with steamed asparagus or grilled salmon fillets.

SmartPoints value: Green plan – 7SP, Blue plan – 5SP, Purple plan – 5SP

Total Time: 26 min, Prep time: 12 min, Cooking time: 14 min, Serves: 4

Nutritional value: Calories – 677.3, Carbs – 29.2g, Fat – 47.8g, Protein - 31.4g

Ingredients

Plain fat-free yogurt - ¼ cup(s)

Reduced-calorie mayonnaise - ¼ cup(s)

Dijon Mustard - 1 tsp

Uncooked Canadian bacon - 4 slice(s)

Lemon zest - ½ tsp

Egg(s) - 4 item(s), large

Fresh lemon juice - 1 tsp

Fresh tomato(es) - 4 slice(s), thick

Unsalted butter - 2 tsp, softened

Chives - 2 Tbsp, chopped fresh (optional)

English muffin - 2 item(s), multigrain or whole wheat variety, split and toasted

White wine vinegar - 1 Tbsp

Instructions

1.   To prepare the sauce, get a small microwavable bowl and whisk yogurt, mayonnaise, mustard, and lemon zest and juice together in the bowl.

2.   Set the microwave to High, and allow the mixture to heat up for about 30 seconds. Remove the bowl from the microwave carefully using your mitts.

3.   Scoop a tablespoon of butter and stir it in until melted. Cover the bowl to keep your sauce warm.

4.   Poach eggs by filling a large, deep skillet with water and allow to boil; add vinegar.

5.   Reduce the heat to a bare simmer. Carefully break the eggs into a custard cup, one at a time, and slip into the hot water.

6. Cook the eggs until the whites are firm, but the yolks are still soft. This process should take about 5 minutes.

7. Transfer the eggs, one at a time, with a slotted spoon to a paper towel-lined plate to drain. Cover the plate to keep the eggs warm.

8. Wipe the skillet dry with a paper towel.

9. Add four slices of Canadian bacon and cook over medium-high heat until they brown in spots, about 60 seconds per side.

10. Place one half each of the English muffins on four plates.

11. Top each with one slice of bacon, one slice of tomato, one poached egg, and about two tablespoons sauce. Speckle with chives, if using.

Note: You can keep the hollandaise sauce warm for up to 40 minutes before serving.

Nut-crusted Mahi-mahi

This recipe sounds fantastic and preparing it is super easy; it only takes about 20 minutes. It works well with just about any thin fish fillet and any kind of nuts. I will like you to add macadamia nuts here for their rich and buttery flavor and because they pair well together with the panko. Also, the mahi-mahi is firm enough to withstand the dredging and roasting. You are free to experiment with whatever you have in your fridge.

SmartPoints value: Green plan - 3SP, Blue plan - 2SP, Purple plan - 2SP

Total Time: 20 min, Prep time: 8 min, Cooking time: 12 min, Serves: 4

Nutritional value: Calories - 234.1, Carbs - 13.9g, Fat - 9.8g, Protein - 24.7g

Ingredients

Cooking spray - 2 spray(s)

Egg white(s) (whipped) - 1 large

Macadamia nuts (dry roasted, salted) - 3 Tbsp, chopped

Mahi-mahi fillet(s) (uncooked) - 1 pound(s), no skin

Parsley (fresh) - 2 Tbsp, or cilantro (fresh, minced)

Plain breadcrumbs (dried) - ¼ cup(s), panko (Japanese variety)

Table salt - ¾ tsp (divided)

Instructions

1.   Prepare the oven by preheating to 450°F. Coat a baking pan with cooking spray and place the container in the oven to heat.

2.   Place some nuts, parsley (or cilantro), panko, and 1/4 tsp of salt in a small blender, then blend all together.

3.   Pour the crumbs into a shallow bowl or plate and set the plate aside.

4.   With the fish placed on a plate, rub 1/2 teaspoon of salt all over it.

5.   Dip the fish into the egg white and turn it to coat. After that, dip the fish into the blended nut mixture and turn to coat.

6.   Remove the pan from the oven and place the coated fish on it.

7.   Roast the fish until the center of the fish is no longer translucent; about 10 to 12 minutes. Serve it immediately once it is ready.

Note: If you desire it, you can garnish with salt and pepper, but that could affect the Smart Points value.

Pan-Fried Flounder

You can serve this dish with homemade fries, or you can add freshly sliced tomatoes alongside. Bear in mind that the cooking time will be different depending on the size of your fillets.

SmartPoints value: Green plan - 4SP, Blue plan - 3SP, Purple plan - 3SP

Total Time: 20 min, Prep time: 14 min, Cooking time: 6 min, Serves: 4

Nutritional value: Calories - 441.2, Carbs - 14.8g, Fat - 30.3g, Protein - 8.3g

Ingredients

Black pepper (freshly ground) - ½ tsp (or to taste)

Cornmeal (yellow) - ¼ cup(s)

Dijon mustard - 1 Tbsp

Egg white(s) (whipped) - 1 large

Lemon(s) - ½ medium, cut into four wedges

Olive oil cooking spray - 2 spray(s)

Olive oil - 1 Tbsp

Parmesan cheese (grated) - 2 Tbsp

Thyme (fresh) - 1 Tbsp, or 1 tsp dried thyme

Table salt - ½ tsp (or to taste)

Uncooked flounder fillet(s) - 1 pound(s)

Instructions

1.   Wash the fish with clean water and pat it dry. Place the fish on a plate and sprinkle both sides of fish with mustard, then dip it into the egg white and set aside.

2.   Mix cornmeal, thyme, Parmesan cheese, salt, and pepper in a medium bowl, then dust the fish with cornmeal-mixture. Ensure that to cover both sides.

3.   Get a large oven-proof skillet and coat it with cooking spray, then set it over medium to medium-high heat. Apply heat to the oil until it starts shimmering.

4.   Add the fish to the skillet and cook for 2 to 3 minutes on one side, then flip the fish and cook until it is ready on the other side; about 2 to 3 minutes.

5.   Serve the fish with your lemon wedges.

Blueberry-Almond Oatmeal

SmartPoints value: Green plan - 3SP, Blue plan - 3SP, Purple plan - 1SP

Total time: 10 min, Prep time: 2 min, Cooking time: 5 min, Serves: 1

Nutritional value: Calories - 340, Carbs - 54g Fat - 8g, Protein - 16g

Ingredients

Blueberries (fresh) - ¼ cup(s)

Almond milk (unsweetened) - 2 Tbsp

Slivered almonds - 2 tsp (toasted)

Old-fashioned rolled oats (such as Quaker Oats) - 1 cup

Milk - 1 cup

Water - 1 cup

Kosher salt - 1/8 tsp

Ground cinnamon - 1/2 tsp

Honey - 1 tsp

Instructions

1.   To prepare oatmeal, combine oats, water, milk, salt, and cinnamon in a medium-sized saucepan. Get it to boil on medium-high heat, and reduce heat to low; about 4-5 min.

2.   Simmer it uncovered until it thickens, occasionally stirring. Remove it from the heat and allow to cool slightly.

3.   Stir blueberries and milk into the oatmeal, then sprinkle it with almonds and cinnamon. Add artificial sweetener to taste if you desire.

Toasted Blueberry Muffin with Warm Citrus Compote

SmartPoints value: Green plan - 4SP, Blue plan - 4SP, Purple plan - 4SP

Total Time: 20 min, Prep time: 10 min, Cooking time: 10 min, Serves: 6

Nutritional value: Calories - 231, Carbs - 36.3g Fat - 7.7g, Protein - 5.2g

Ingredients

Brown sugar (Splenda) blend - 1 tsp

Cornstarch - 1 Tbsp

Water - 2 Tbsp

Orange juice (fresh) - ½ cup(s)

Orange sections - 1 cup(s), divided

Vanilla extract - ⅛ teaspoon

Lemon zest - ⅛ teaspoon

Lime zest - ⅛ teaspoon

WW Blueberry muffin - 3 item(s)

Instructions

1.   Prepare the oven by preheating to 350°F.

2.   Whisk cornstarch, brown sugar, and water together in a medium-sized saucepan.

3.   Whip the mixture in orange juice. While whipping constantly, bring the mixture to a boil over medium heat; about 2 minutes. The mixture will thicken rapidly, so make sure to whisk continuously to prevent lumps.

4.   Whisk the thick mixture in half cup of orange segments and continue to simmer over medium-low heat for another 6 to 8 minutes, stirring it regularly. The orange sections should break down, and the sauce should become thick, but it should not stiffen up.

5.   Drop the thick sauce from the heat and stir in vanilla extract, lemon zest, and lime zest. Allow it to cool off for about 10 minutes.

6.   While the sauce is getting cooled, cut each muffin in half and toast them in the oven lightly on both sides.

7.   Serve each person half a muffin topped with two tablespoons of compote. Garnish them with the remaining half cup of orange segments.

Notes: You can also use leftover compote as a delicious breakfast marmalade. Spread it on whole-wheat toast, apple slices, or stir it into fat-free plain yogurt. Preserve the leftover compote in an airtight container inside a refrigerator for up to 3 days.

Cuban Black Beans and Rice

SmartPoints value: Green plan - 7SP, Blue plan - 4SP, Purple plan - 4SP

Total Time: 35 min, Prep time: 10 min, Cooking time: 25 min, Serves: 6

Nutritional value: Calories - 333.5, Carbs - 54.8g Fat - 5.1g, Protein - 16.1g

Ingredients

Water - 2½ cup(s), divided

Uncooked white rice (long grain-variety) - 1 cup(s)

Olive oil - 2 tsp

Banana pepper(s) - 1 medium

Black beans (canned) - 31 oz, two 15.5 oz cans (undrained)

Cilantro (fresh, chopped, divided) - ⅔ cup(s)

Minced garlic - 1½ Tbsp

Ground cumin - 1 tsp

Uncooked red onion(s) (chopped) - 1¾ cup(s)

Oregano (dried) - 1 tsp

Table salt - 1 tsp (or to taste)

Red wine vinegar - 1 Tbsp

Lime(s) (fresh) - 1 medium, cut into six wedges

Instructions

1.   Bring two cups of water to a boil in a small saucepan and add the rice, then cook as package directs.

2.   Heat some oil in a large nonstick skillet over medium-high heat.

3.   Add a cup of chopped onions and all of the pepper, then cook, occasionally stirring, until it is tender; about 7 minutes.

4.   Toss in garlic, cumin, and oregano, then cook, stirring until fragrant; about 30 seconds.

5.   Stir in the beans and their liquid, the remaining half cup of water and salt, then bring to a simmer.

6.   Reduce the heat to low and simmer for the flavors to blend in about 5 minutes.

7.   Remove the dish from heat, then stir in vinegar and 1/3 cup of cilantro.

8.   To serve, use a spoon to put beans over rice and sprinkle it with 1/4 cup of the remaining onion and 1/3 cup of the remaining cilantro, then squeeze fresh lime juice over the top.

Note: If you desire, sprinkle the dish with salt before serving.

Spaghetti Squash with Fresh Tomato-Basil Sauce

SmartPoints value: Green plan - 2SP, Blue plan - 2SP, Purple plan - 2SP

Total time: 30 min, Prep time: 15 min, Cooking time: 15 min, Serves: 4

Nutritional value: Calories - 216.2, Carbs - 14.2g Fat - 17.2g, Protein - 5.0g

Enjoy this recipe with its taste of summer. Ensure to cook it with very ripe tomatoes and fresh basil to get the best flavour.

Ingredients

Tomato(es) (fresh) - 2¼ pound(s)

Olive oil (extra virgin) - 2 Tbsp

Minced garlic - 1¼ tsp, finely minced

Basil (fresh, sliced) - ½ cup(s)

Kosher salt - ½ tsp (or to taste)

Black pepper (freshly ground) - ¼ tsp (or to taste)

Spaghetti squash (uncooked) - 2½ pound(s)

Instructions

1.   Toss tomatoes, oil, garlic, basil, salt and pepper together in a large bowl and let it stand, occasionally tossing, until the tomatoes release their juices and the mixture is quite juicy; about 10 to 15 minutes.

2.   Cut the spaghetti squash in half and scoop out the seeds, then place the squash in a covered microwave-safe container.

3.   Cook the spaghetti squash on high power until strands of squash separate when you scrape the flesh with a fork; about 15 minutes. Alternatively, you can also roast the squash for about 20 minutes in the oven.

4.   Scrape the spaghetti squash from the peel with a fork to form strands and add it to the bowl with tomatoes and toss to coat.

Notes: It would be delicious to add chunks of fresh mozzarella or freshly grated Parmesan cheese to this meal. However, it might affect the Smart Points value.

Sweet Corn Soup

Nutritional Facts

servings per container	5
Prep Total	**10 min**
Serving Size 2/3 cup (27g)	
Amount per serving **Calories**	**200**
	% Daily Value
Total Fat 8g	**1%**
Saturated Fat 1g	2%
Trans Fat 0g	2%
Cholesterol	**2%**
Sodium 240mg	**7%**
Total Carbohydrate 12g	**2%**
Dietary Fiber 4g	14%
Total Sugar 12g	01.21%
Protein 3g	
Vitamin C 2mcg	2%
Calcium 20mg	1%
Iron 7mg	2%
Potassium 25mg	6%

Ingredients

6 ears of corn

1 tablespoon of corn oil

1 small onion

1/2 cup grated celery root

7 cups water or vegetable stock

Add salt to taste

Instructions:

1. Shuck the corn & slice off the kernels

2. In a large soup pot put in the oil, onion, celery root, and one cup of water

3. Let that mixture stew under low heat until the onion is soft

4. Include the corn, salt & remaining water and bring it to a boil

5. Cool briefly & then puree in a blender, then wait for it to cool before putting it through a food mill.

6. Reheat & add salt with pepper to taste nice.

Mexican Avocado Salad

Nutritional Facts

servings per container	6
Prep Total	**10 min**
Serving Size 2/3 cup (70g)	
Amount per serving **Calories**	**120**
	% Daily Value
Total Fat 8g	**10%**
Saturated Fat 1g	8%
Trans Fat 0g	21
Cholesterol	**22%**
Sodium 16mg	**7%**
Total Carbohydrate 7g	**13%**
Dietary Fiber 4g	14%
Total Sugar 1g	-
Protein 2g	
Vitamin C 1mcg	1%
Calcium 260mg	20%
Iron 2mg	25%
Potassium 235mg	6%

Ingredients

24 cherry tomatoes, quartered

2 tablespoon extra-virgin olive oil

4 teaspoons red wine vinegar

2 teaspoon salt

¼ teaspoon freshly ground black pepper

Gently chopped ½ medium yellow or white onion

1 jalapeño, seeded & finely chopped

2 tablespoons chopped fresh cilantro

¼ medium head iceberg lettuce, cut into ½-inch ribbons
Chopped 2 ripe Hass avocados, seeded, peeled

Instructions:

1.   Add tomatoes, oil, vinegar, salt, & pepper in a neat medium bowl. Add onion, jalapeño & cilantro; toss well

2.   Put lettuce on a platter & top with avocado

3.   Spoon tomato mixture on top and serve.

Crazy Delicious Raw Pad Thai

Nutritional Facts

servings per container	3
Prep Total	**10 min**
Serving Size 2/3 cup (77g)	
Amount per serving **Calories**	**210**
	% Daily Value
Total Fat 3g	**10%**
Saturated Fat 2g	8%
Trans Fat 7g	-
Cholesterol	**0%**
Sodium 120mg	7%
Total Carbohydrate 77g	**10%**
Dietary Fiber 4g	14%
Total Sugar 12g	-
Protein 3g	
Vitamin C 1mcg	20%
Calcium 260mg	20%
Iron 2mg	41%
Potassium 235mg	1%

Ingredients

2 large zucchini

Thinly sliced ¼ red cabbage

Chopped ¼ cup fresh mint leaves

Sliced 1 spring onion

peeled and sliced ½ avocado

10 raw almonds

4 tablespoonful sesame seeds Dressing

¼ cup peanut butter

2 tablespoonful tahini

2 lemon, juiced

2 tablespoonful tamari / salt-reduced soy sauce and add ½ chopped green chili

Instructions:

1. Collect dressing ingredients in a container

2. Pop the top on and shake truly well to join. I like mine pleasant and smooth however you can include a dash of sifted water on the off chance that it looks excessively thick.

3. Using a mandoline or vegetable peeler, expel one external portion of skin from every zucchini and dispose of.

4. Combine zucchini strips, cabbage & dressing in a vast blending bowl and blend well

5. Divide zucchini blend between two plates or bowls

6. Top with residual fixings and appreciate!

Kale and Wild Rice Stir Fly

Nutritional Facts

servings per container	3
Prep Total	**10 min**
Serving Size 2/3 cup (80g)	
Amount per serving **Calories**	**220**
	% Daily Value
Total Fat 5g	**22%**
Saturated Fat 1g	8%
Trans Fat 0g	-
Cholesterol	**0%**
Sodium 200mg	7%

Ingredients

1 tablespoonful extra virgin olive oil

Diced ¼ onion

3 carrots, cut into ½ inch slices

2 cups assorted mushrooms

2 bunch kale, chopped into bite-sized pieces

2 tablespoonful lemon juice

2 tablespoonful chili flakes, more if desired

1 tablespoon Braggs Liquid Aminos

2 cup wild rice, cooked

Instructions:

1. In a large sauté pan, heat oil over on heater. Include onion & cook until translucent, for 35 to 10 minutes.

2. Include carrots & sauté for another 2 minutes. Include mushrooms & cook for 4 minutes. Include kale, lemon juice, chili flakes & Braggs. Cook until kale is slightly wilted.

3. Serve over wild rice and enjoy your Lunch!

Creamy Avocado Pasta

servings per container	7
Prep Total	**10 min**
Serving Size 2/3 cup (25g)	
Amount per serving **Calories**	19
	% Daily Value
Total Fat 8g	300%
Saturated Fat 1g	40%
Trans Fat 0g	20%
Cholesterol	6%
Sodium 210mg	3%
Total Carbohydrate 22g	400%
Dietary Fiber 4g	1%
Total Sugar 12g	02.20%
Protein 3g	
Vitamin C 2mcg	20%
Calcium 10mg	6%
Iron 4mg	7%
Potassium 25mg	6%

Ingredients

340 g / 12 oz spaghetti

2 ripe avocados, halved, seeded & neatly peeled 1/2 cup fresh basil leaves

3 cloves garlic

1/3 cup olive oil

2-3 teaspoon freshly squeezed lemon juice

Add sea salt & black pepper, to taste

1.5 cups cherry tomatoes, halved

Instructions:

1.   In a large pot of boiling salted water, cook pasta according to the package. When al dente, drain and set aside.

2.   To make the avocado sauce, combine avocados, basil, garlic, oil, and lemon juice in food processor. Blend on high until smooth. Season with salt and pepper to taste.

3.   In a large bowl, combine pasta, avocado sauce, and cherry tomatoes until evenly coated.

4.   To serve, top with additional cherry tomatoes, fresh basil, or lemon zest.

5.   Best when fresh. Avocado will oxidize over time so store leftovers in a covered container in refrigerator up to one day.

Zucchini Pasta with Pesto Sauce

Nutritional Facts

servings per container	5
Prep Total	**10 min**
Serving Size 2/3 cup (20g)	
Amount per serving **Calories**	**100**
	% Daily Value
Total Fat 8g	**12%**
Saturated Fat 1g	2%
Trans Fat 0g	20%
Cholesterol	**2%**
Sodium 10mg	7%
Total Carbohydrate 7g	**2%**
Dietary Fiber 2g	14%
Total Sugar 1g	01.20%
Protein 3g	
Vitamin C 2mcg	10%
Calcium 240mg	1%
Iron 2mg	2%
Potassium 25mg	6%

Ingredients

1 to 2 medium zucchini (make noodles with a mandoline or Spiralizer)

1/2 teaspoon of salt

For Pesto

33

soaked 1/4 cup cashews

soaked 1/4 cup pine nuts

1/2 cup spinach

1/2 cup peas you can make it fresh or frozen one

1/4 cup broccoli

1/4 cup basil leaves

1/2 avocado

1 or 2 tablespoons original olive oil

2 tablespoons nutritional yeast

1/2 teaspoon salt

Pinch black pepper

Instructions:

1.   Place zucchini noodles in a strainer over a clean bowl

2.   Include 1/2 teaspoon of salt & let it set while preparing the pesto sauce

3.   Mix all the ingredients for the pesto sauce

4.   Extract excess water from zucchini noodles & place them in a clean bowl

5.   Pour the sauce on top & garnish with some basil leaves & pine nut

Balsamic BBQ Seitan and Tempeh Ribs

Nutritional Facts

servings per container	4
Prep Total	**10 min**
Serving Size 2/3 cup (56g)	
Amount per serving **Calories**	**100**
	% Daily Value
Total Fat 7g	**1%**
Saturated Fat 1g	2%
Trans Fat 0g	20%
Cholesterol	**2%**
Sodium 160mg	**7%**
Total Carbohydrate 37g	**2%**
Dietary Fiber 2g	1%
Total Sugar 2g	01.20%
Protein 14g	
Vitamin C 1mcg	10%
Calcium 450mg	1%
Iron 2mg	2%
Potassium 35mg	7%

Ingredients

For the spice rub

Minced ¼ cup fresh parsley

Instructions:

1.   In a clean bowl, join the ingredients for the spice rub. Blend well & put aside.

2.   In a small saucepan over medium heat, combine the apple juice vinegar, balsamic vinegar, maple syrup, ketchup, red onion, garlic, and chile. Mix & let stew, revealed, for around 60 minutes. Increase the level of the heat to medium-high & cook for 15 additional minutes until the sauce thickens. Mix it frequently. In the event that it appears to be excessively thick, include some water.

3.   Preheat the oven to 350 degrees. In a clean bowl, join the dry ingredients for the seitan & blend well. In a clean bowl, add the wet ingredients. Add the wet ingredients to the dry & blend until simply consolidated. Manipulate the dough gently until everything is combined & the dough feels elastic.

4.   Grease or shower a preparing dish. Include the dough to the baking dish, smoothing it & stretching it to fit the dish. Cut the dough into 7 to 9 strips & afterward down the middle to make 16 thick ribs.

5.   Top the dough with the flavor rub & back rub it in a bit. Heat the seitan for 40 minutes to an hour or until the seitan has a strong surface to it. Remove the dish from the heater. Recut the strips & cautiously remove them from the baking dish.

6.   Increase the oven temperature to about 400 degrees. Slather the ribs with BBQ sauce & lay them on a baking sheet. Set the ribs back in the heater for pretty much 12 minutes so the sauce can get a bit roasted. Then again, you can cook the sauce-covered ribs on a grill or in a grill pan.

Green Bean Casserole

Nutritional Facts

Serving per container	2
Prep Total	**10 min**
Serving Size 2/3 cup (5g)	
Amount per serving **Calories**	**100**
	% Daily Value
Total Fat 10g	**12%**
Saturated Fat 2g	2%
Trans Fat 4g	20%
Cholesterol	**2%**
Sodium 70mg	**7%**
Total Carbohydrate 18g	**2%**
Dietary Fiber 9g	10%
Total Sugar 16g	01.20%
Protein 2g	
Vitamin C 9mcg	10%
Calcium 720mg	1%
Iron 6mg	2%
Potassium 150mg	6%

Ingredients

Diced 1 large onion

3 tablespoons of original olive oil

¼ cup flour

2 cups of water

1 tablespoon of salt

½ tablespoons of garlic powder

1 or 2 bags frozen green beans (10 ounces each)

1 fried onion

Instructions:

1.   Preheat oven to 350 degrees.

2.   Heat original olive oil in a shallow pan. Include onion & stir occasionally while the onions soften and turn translucent. This takes about 15 to 20 minutes, don't rush it because it gives so much flavor! Once onion is well cooked, include flour & stir well to cook flour. It will be a dry mixture. Include salt & garlic powder. Add some water. Let simmer for about 1 – 2 minutes & allow mixture to thicken. Immediately remove from heat

3.   Pour green beans into a square baking dish & add 2/3 can of onions. Include all of the gravy & stir well to together

4.   Place in oven & cook for 25 to 30 minutes, gravy mixture will be bubbly. Top with remaining fried onions & cook for 4 to 12 minutes more. Serve immediately and enjoy your dinner.

Socca Pizza [Vegan]

Nutritional Facts

servings per container	2
Prep Total	**10 min**
Serving Size 2/3 cup (78g)	
Amount per serving **Calories**	**120**
	% Daily Value
Total Fat 10g	**20%**
Saturated Fat 5g	7%
Trans Fat 6g	27%
Cholesterol	**5%**
Sodium 10mg	**10%**
Total Carbohydrate 4g	**20%**
Dietary Fiber 9g	15%
Total Sugar 12g	01.70%
Protein 6g	
Vitamin C 7mcg	10%
Calcium 290mg	20%
Iron 4mg	2%
Potassium 240mg	7%

Ingredients

Socca Base

1 cup chickpea (garbanzo bean) flour – I used bob's Red Mill Garbanzo Fava Flour

1 or 2 cups of cold, filtered water

1 to 2 tablespoons minced garlic

½ tablespoon of sea salt

2 tablespoons coconut oil (for greasing)

Toppings

Add Tomato-paste

Add Dried Italian herbs (oregano, basil, thyme, rosemary, etc.)

Add Mushrooms

Add Red onion

Add Capsicum/bell pepper

Add Sun-dried tomatoes

Add Kalamata olives

Add Vegan Cheese & Chopped Fresh basil leaves

Instructions:

1.   Pre-heat oven to 350F

2.   In a clean mixing bowl, whisk together garbanzo bean flour & water until there are no lumps remaining. Stir together in garlic 7 sea salt. Allow resting for about 12 minutes to thicken.

3.   Grease 2 - 4 small, shallow dishes/tins with original coconut oil

4.   Pour mixture into a clean dish & bake for about 20 - 15 minutes or until golden brown.

5.   Remove dishes from oven, top with your favorite toppings & vegan cheese (optional) & return to the oven for another 7 - 10 minutes or so.

6.   Remove dishes from oven & allow to sit for a about 2 – 5 minutes before removing pizzas from the dishes. Enjoy your dinner!

Salads, Soups, and Sandwiches

For me, soups and stews are always best for winter. Perfect meals for lunch are those low in fat and calories naturally. That is why I love soups and stews; when I want to make it more of a main dish for dinner, it's best to add protein.

The hearty ingredients are so satisfying, and that makes eating them more deliberate. Opt for any of these deliciously prepared recipes of lean protein and savor the flavors.

Easy Egg Salad

There are different ways to prepare eggs as a snack. They are all fabulous, especially since they are Zero Smart Points. I adore my easy egg salad recipe because it's simple, and you can prepare it with just a handful of ingredients. You must have noticed that I like easy-to-cook recipes.

This egg salad doesn't need mayonnaise! Just a few ingredients make a healthy snack. Savor the flavors.

SmartPoints value: Green plan - 2SP, Blue plan - 2SP, Purple plan - 2SP

Total time: 5 min, Prep time: 5 min, Serves: 2

Nutritional value: Calories - 229, Carbs - 3g, Fat - 17g, Protein - 12g

Ingredients

Hard-boiled eggs - 4 pieces

Olive oil - 1 tbsp

Onions (diced) - 1/3 cup

Paprika - ½ tsp

Pepper and salt to taste

Instructions

1.   Grate the peeled egg using a cheese grater

2.   Mix the eggs, olive oil, onion, pepper and salt in a bowl

3.   Feel free to try several combinations and find your favorite. You could try toppings like tomatoes, dill, parsley, chives, relish, pickles, olives, bell peppers, or avocados.

Summer Green Bean Salad

I've seen some people cook their green beans until they are limp as a dishcloth. However, I like it when my green beans are just a little crispy. To keep them crispy, I blanch them in boiling water for about 3 minutes and then immediately put them in an ice bath; if I don't do that, the beans will get overcooked.

This salad is a sure hit regardless of where you got the green beans, either from your garden or from the grocery store. I usually end up eating most of all of this salad the very first night. I'm not sure you'll be lucky to have some leftovers. Often, salads get gross in the fridge overnight. The greens become unappealing. But, since I made this salad with fresh, crisp veggies, it's still as good the next day.

SmartPoints value: Green plan - 1SP, Blue plan - 1SP, Purple plan - 1SP

Total time: 18 min, Prep time: 15 min, Cooking time: 3 min, Serves:

Nutritional value: Calories - 69, Carbs – 9.1g, Fat – 3.7g, Protein - 2g

Ingredients

Green beans (fresh, cut into pieces) - (1 lb)

Red onion (thinly sliced) - 1/2

Cherry tomatoes (halved) - 1 1/2 cups

Basil (finely chopped, fresh) - 1/2 cup

Garlic (minced) - 2 cloves

Olive oil - 1 1/2 tbsp

Lemon juice - 1 cup

Pepper and salt to taste

Instructions

1.   Boil a pot of water and blanch the green beans in the water for about 3 minutes. Drain the beans and transfer to an ice bath for about 2-3 minutes, then place the dried green beans in a large bowl.

2.   Put the remaining ingredients and toss thoroughly.

3.   Enjoy!

Chopped Greek Salad with Creamy Yogurt Dressing

This refreshingly cDashchy salad has the ingredients of a Greek salad, but it is deliciously different as it contains creamy yogurt.

SmartPoints value: Green plan - 4SP, Blue plan - 4SP, Purple plan - 4SP

Total Time: 20 min, Prep time: 2 min, Cooking time: 18 min, Serves: 6

Nutritional value: Calories - 29.0, Carbs - 0.5g Fat - 2.7g, Protein - 0.8g

Ingredients

Black pepper (freshly ground) - ¼ tsp (or to taste)

Low-fat yogurt (plain) - ¾ cup(s), (not Greek)

Crumbled feta cheese - ½ cup(s)

Dill (fresh, chopped) - 1 Tbsp

Water - 3 Tbsp

Olive oil (extra virgin) - 2 Tbsp

Lemon zest - 1 tsp

Lemon juice (fresh) - 1 Tbsp, (or to taste)

Garlic cloves (very finely minced) - 1 small clove(s)

Oregano (dried) - 1 tsp

Table salt - ½ tsp (or to taste)

Cucumber(s) (English variety, diced) - 1 medium

Yellow pepper(s) (diced) - 2 medium

Grape tomatoes - 2 cup(s), halved

Mint leaves (fresh) - ¾ cup(s), leaves, torn

Uncooked red onion(s) - ⅓ cup(s), chopped

Olive(s) (pitted, sliced) - 12 medium, Kalamata

Instructions

1.   Cut the tomatoes in half, and dice the cucumber, peppers, and onion. Set it aside.

2.   Whip yogurt, oil, water, lemon zest, and juice together in a clean small bowl, then add garlic, dill, oregano, salt, and pepper.

3.   Combine the remaining ingredients inside a large bowl and toss them together. Add the mixture to the dressing, then toss to coat.

Roasted Beet and Wheat Berry Salad

Wheat berries are grains that are rich in fibre, with a chewy texture. They're delicious when paired with roasted beets and creamy goat cheese, but you can use feta if you prefer. For added convenience, you can cook both beets and wheatberries several days in advance of serving this salad. Simply heat them again and add to the remaining ingredients when you want to assemble the salad. You can decide to serve this salad warm, at room temperature, or chilled.

SmartPoints value: Green plan: 6SP, Blue plan: 6SP, Purple plan: 3SP Total Time: 60 min, Prep time: 20 min, Cooking time: 40 min, Serves: 6 Nutritional value: Calories - 141.4, Carbs - 22.8g Fat - 5.0g, Protein - 6.4g

Ingredients

Cooking spray - 3 spray(s)

Beets (uncooked) - 2 pound(s), red or golden (scrubbed)

Kosher salt - 2½ tsp, divided

Wheat berries (uncooked) - 1 cup(s)

Orange juice (unsweetened) - 2 Tbsp

Orange marmalade - 1 Tbsp

Olive oil (extra-virgin) - 1 Tbsp

Apple cider vinegar - 1 Tbsp

Scallion(s)(uncooked) - ½ cup(s), sliced (white and light green parts), or to taste

Parsley (fresh) - ⅓ cup(s), flat-leaf, chopped, or to taste

Goat cheese (semisoft) - ⅓ cup(s), crumbled

Table salt - ¼ tsp (or to taste)

Black pepper - ¼ tsp (or to taste)

Instructions

1.   Prepare the oven by heating to 400°F. Coat a clean baking pan with cooking spray.

2.   Place beets on the prepared baking pan and lightly coat with cooking spray. Sprinkle the beets with a half teaspoon of salt and tightly cover with foil, then roast until tender; about 40 min.

3.   Remove the pan from the oven and allow beets to cool slightly,

then gently remove the skin with a knife.

4.   Dice the beets or cut into thick matchsticks and set aside.

5.   Cover wheatberries with two inches of water in a small saucepan and stir in one teaspoon of salt, then bring it to a boil.

6.   Reduce the heat to low, cover it, and simmer until the wheat berries are tender; about 50 - 60 minutes. Drain the saucepan and set aside.

7.   To make a vinaigrette, mix orange juice, marmalade, oil, vinegar and remaining teaspoon salt in a small bowl, while the beets and wheatberries cook.

8.   Use a clean spoon to put the wheat berries into a serving bowl and gently toss them with the beets, vinaigrette, scallions and parsley, then season to taste with salt and pepper.

9.   Garnish the dish with goat cheese and serve.

Italian Pasta Salad with Tomatoes and Artichoke Hearts

SmartPoints value: Green plan - 5SP, Blue plan - 5SP, Purple plan - 5SP

Total Time: 28 min, Prep time: 18 min, Cooking time: 10 min, Serves: 6

Nutritional value: Calories - 296.2, Carbs - 47.3g Fat - 8.2g, Protein - 8.7g

The best time to make this pasta salad is at the height of summer when fresh tomatoes are at their glorious, unrivalled peak. Make sure you use the ripest, juiciest tomatoes you can find. Tomato juices will add a delicious flavour to the dressing.

The chopped artichoke hearts will add a briny taste to every bite. Cellentani pasta is the macaroni formed into a spiral shape, also known as cavatappi. If you can't find that variety, feel free to use whatever type you can get, although short kinds of pasta like penne, rotini, and macaroni would work best. Turn this into a meal by adding some grilled or sautéed chicken or shrimp.

Ingredients

Tomato(es) (fresh) - 1 pound(s), ripe beefsteak or Campari, chopped (3 cups)

Bell pepper(s) (uncooked) - 2 item(s), small, yellow and orange, diced (1 ½ cups)

Artichoke hearts without oil (canned) - 14 oz, drained, roughly chopped

Basil (torn or coarsely chopped) - 1 cup(s)

Red wine vinegar - 2 Tbsp

Olive oil (extra virgin) - 2 Tbsp

Table salt - ½ tsp, with extra for cooking pasta

Black pepper - ½ tsp, freshly ground

Garlic powder - ¼ tsp, or more to taste

Pasta (uncooked) - 6 oz, cellentani recommended (2 cups)
Parmesan cheese (shredded) - ⅓ cup(s), or shaved, divided

Instructions

1.   Combine artichoke hearts, basil, tomatoes, peppers, vinegar, oil, salt, pepper, and garlic powder in a large bowl, then toss to coat. Allow the pasta to stand while cooking, occasionally tossing.

2.   Boil a pot of well-salted water and cook the pasta according to package directions. Drain and rinse it with cold water, then drain again.

3.   Add the pasta to the bowl with tomato mixture and toss to coat. Add all but two Tbsp Parmesan and toss again.

4.   Serve the pasta salad with the remaining cheese sprinkled over to the top.

Tofu-veggie Kebabs with Peanut-sriracha Sauce

SmartPoints value: Green plan: 7SP, Blue plan - 3SP, Purple plan - 3SP

Total Time: 41 min, Prep time: 35 min, Cooking time: 6 min, Serves: 4

Nutritional value: Calories - 144.7, Carbs - 9.5g Fat - 8.9g, Protein - 8.8g

Are you planning to go meatless at your next barbecue? Veggie kebabs are your perfect companion. These broccoli, tofu, and radish favorites offer a delicious option for a vegetarian, vegan, or someone who demands a fresher take on the usual cookout. Put the kebabs together quickly in the kitchen.

Then, brush them with an easy-to-make savory sauce before placing them on the grill. Powdered peanut butter makes this nutritious sauce that adds loads of flavor to the favorites.

Cooking them takes about six minutes, and they are perfect for your next picnic. You can pair them with a fresh side salad to increase the vegetable tally.

Ingredients

Broccoli (uncooked) - 10 oz, florets (about 4 cups)

Cooking spray - 4 spray(s)

Firm tofu (rinsed and drained) - 28 oz

Table salt - ½ tsp

Radish(es) (fresh, trimmed and halved) - 8 medium

Lime juice (fresh) - 1½ Tbsp

Peanut butter (powdered) - 6 Tbsp

Water - 4½ Tbsp

Ketchup - 3 Tbsp

White miso - 3 Tbsp, (low-sodium)

Soy sauce (low-sodium) - 1½ Tbsp

Sriracha hot sauce - 1½ tsp

Sesame oil (toasted) - 1½ tsp

Sesame seeds (unsalted toasted) - 1 Tbsp

Instructions

1.   Soak up to eight 10-inches bamboo skewers in a shallow dish containing water for at least 20 minutes (or use metal skewers).

2.   Put water in a large saucepan and bring it to a boil over high heat. Add salt and radishes to the pan and cook for 5 minutes.

3.   Add broccoli and cook for 1 minute more. Drain a colander into the saucepan and its content, then Dash the vegetables under cold water until it is cool to the touch. Drain it properly; Pat it dry with paper towels.

4.   Dry out the tofu blocks with paper towels and cut each block into 12 even cubes.

5.   To prepare the sauce, stir the water and powdered peanut butter together in a medium bowl to form a smooth, loose paste.

6.   Add lime juice, ketchup, miso, Sriracha, soy sauce, and oil, then stir to mix.

7.   To prepare kebabs, thread two broccoli florets, two radish halves, and three tofu cubes on each skewer.

8.   Apply medium-high heat to a grill. Brush the kebabs with sauce on one side and lightly coat with cooking spray off the heat.

9.   Place the kebabs on the grill, sauce side down and cook for 2-3 minutes.

10.   Brush the other side with the sauce, flip it and cook for another 2-3 minutes.

11.   Remove the kebabs from the grill and brush them with extra sauce, then sprinkle them with sesame seeds before serving.

Crockpot Beef Stew

Using a crockpot for stew is not just comfortable but also guarantees that I don't burn it to the bottom of the pot. I love the fact that I can refrigerate my stew in the crockpot overnight, and the next morning, all I need to do is put it in the crockpot base and turn it on. If you are thinking of a fitting meal for a cold winter evening, give this beef stew a try. It is one of the highly-rated meals over time. I believe the taste will leave you wanting more.

SmartPoints value: Green plan - 6SP, Blue plan - 6SP, Purple plan - 6SP

SmartPoints value: Green plan - 6SP, Blue plan - 6SP, Purple plan - 6SP

Total Time: 1hr 15min, Prep time: 15 min, Cooking time: 1hr, Serves: 8

Nutritional value: Calories – 343, Carbs – 23.5g, Fat – 17.3g, Protein – 22.2g

Ingredients

Beef chuck roast - 2 lb

Russet potatoes (2-in diameter) - 4 medium

Carrots - 4 medium

Onion - 1 large

Garlic - 4 cloves

Onion soup mix - 1 packet

Fat-free beef broth - 8 cups

Celery stalks (chopped) - 4 medium

Add salt and pepper (to taste)

Instructions

1.   Chop the roast into pieces (1 inch)

2.   Cut peeled potatoes into slices (1/2 inch)

3.   Cut peeled carrots into equal chunks (1/2 inch)

4.   Cut onion into large pieces

5.   Mix the beef, celery, carrots, potatoes, onion, garlic, onion soup mix and beef broth inside the crockpot

6.   Add seasoning to taste (salt and pepper)

7.   Cook till it's ready

8.   This meal is easy to prepare. All you need to do is give it a try and enjoy it.

Chicken, Lentil, and Spinach Soup

SmartPoints value: Green plan - 1SP, Blue plan - 1SP, Purple plan - 1SP

Total Time: 1hr 10min, Prep time: 10 min, Cooking time: 1hr, Serves: 6

Nutritional value: Calories – 254, Carbs – 27g, Fat – 4.8g, Protein – 26g

As I said earlier, soups and stews are great for me during fall and winter, but this chicken, lentil, and spinach could also serve as spring meals. Though not as rich and heavy as other soups, it is quite substantial.

Ingredients

Chicken breast - 1 lb

French dried (green lentils) - 1 cup

Fresh spinach - One 6 oz package

Finely chopped onion (1 piece)

Carrots (chopped) - 2 pieces

Stalk of celery (chopped) - 2 pieces

Garlic (chopped) - 6 cloves

Olive oil (1 tbsp)

Tomato paste - 2 tbsp

Paprika - 1 tsp

Chicken broth or water - 6 cups (fat-free)

Fresh lemon juice – Half a cup

Add salt and pepper to taste

Instructions

1.   Use medium heat to heat olive oil in a large pot or Dutch oven

2.   Put carrots, celery, onions, and garlic and cook till about minutes when vegetables begin to soften

3. Coat the vegetables with the tomato paste and cover till about 2-3 minutes when the paste begins to darken.

4. Stir lentils, paprika, salt, and pepper in the broth or water and bring to a boil and add in the chicken, then cook for about 5 minutes.

5. Cover and cook for about 35 – 45 minutes on medium-low heat until chicken cooks and lentil are tender but not mushy. Make sure the soup is not bubbling or boiling much as you stir periodically.

6. Shred the chicken breasts using two forks. Stir in spinach and lemon juice and cook for about 2 minutes until the spinach wilts. Turn off the heat and add additional salt and pepper to taste.

7. To enjoy the chicken stew and leave it in mind as your best, do not overcook the lentils. Keep an eye on it and make sure they are tender but firm.

Roasted Tomato Basil Soup

SmartPoints value: Green plan - 4SP, Blue plan - 4SP, Purple plan - 4SP

Total Time: 1hr 20min, Prep time: 10 min, Cooking time: 1hr 10mins

Serves: 4

Nutritional value: Calories – 238, Carbs – 26.1g, Fat – 3g, Protein – 5g

Most tomato soups are creamy but unfortunately has lots of fat, but this roasted tomato basil soup makes the difference. You might just say goodbye to canned tomato soup after enjoying the fresh flavors of roasted tomato basil soup.

Ingredients

Plum tomatoes (halved) - 2 lbs

Plum tomatoes in their juice - One 14 oz can

Olive oil - 1 tbsp

Onion (diced) - 1 large

Minced garlic (4 cloves)

Butter (2 tbsp)

Red pepper flakes (crushed) - 1/8 tsp

Vegetable stock - 3 cups

Basil (fresh) - 2 cups

Oregano (dried) - 1 tsp

Salt and pepper as desired

Instructions

1.   Line a rimmed baking sheet with parchment paper on a 400-degree preheated oven. Before placing them on the baking sheet, toss the tomatoes and garlic cloves with olive oil. Then roast for about 35-45 minutes or until tomatoes are charred.

2.   Using medium heat, heat the butter in a stockpot or Dutch, then add onions and red pepper flakes. Sauté until the onion starts to brown.

3.   In the canned tomato, stir the basil, oregano, and stock or water. Then, add in the oven-roasted tomatoes and garlic, including any juices on the baking sheet. Boil and simmer uncovered for about 25-30, then stir regularly.

4.   Until you reach the desired consistency, process the soup using an immersion blender.

5.   Add salt and pepper to taste.

Seafood-Stuffed Salmon Fillets

All out Time

Prep: 25 min. Heat: 20 min.

Makes

12 servings

Nutritional Facts: 1 stuffed filet: 454 calories, 27g fat (6g immersed fat), 123mg cholesterol, 537mg sodium, 9g starch (0 sugars, 0 filaments), and 41g protein.

Ingredients

1-1/2 cups cooked long-grain rice

1 bundle (8 ounces) impersonation crabmeat

2 tablespoons cream cheddar, relaxed

2 tablespoons margarine, dissolved

2 garlic cloves, minced

1/2 teaspoon each dried basil, marjoram, oregano, thyme, and rosemary, squashed

1/2 teaspoon celery seed, squashed

12 salmon filets (8 ounces each and 1-1/2 inches thick)

3 tablespoons olive oil

2 teaspoons dill weed

1-1/2 teaspoons salt

Direction

1.   Preheat stove to 400°. In an enormous bowl, join rice, crab, cream cheddar, spread, garlic, basil, marjoram, oregano, thyme, rosemary and celery seed.

2.   Cut a pocket on a level plane in each filet to inside 1/2 in. of the inverse side. Load up with stuffing blend; secure with toothpicks. Spot salmon on 2 lubed 15x10x1-in. heating skillet. Brush with oil; sprinkle with dill and salt.

3.   Bake 18-22 minutes or until fish just starts to chip effectively with a fork. Dispose of toothpicks before serving.

Classic Crab Boil

All out Time

Prep: 10 min. Cook: 30 min.

Makes

2 servings

Nutritional Facts: 1 crab: 245 calories, 3g fat (0 immersed fats), 169mg cholesterol, 956mg sodium, 2g starch (0 sugars, 0 fiber), 50g protein.

Ingredients

2 tablespoons mustard seed

2 tablespoons celery seed

1 tablespoon dill seed

1 tablespoon coriander seeds

1 tablespoon entire allspice

1/2 teaspoon entire cloves

4 cove leaves

Cheesecloth

8 quarts water

1/4 cup salt

1/4 cup lemon juice

1 teaspoon cayenne pepper

2 entire live Dungeness crab (2 pounds each)

Melted margarine and lemon wedges

Directions

1.   Place the initial seven fixings on a twofold thickness of cheesecloth. Assemble corners of fabric to encase seasonings; tie safely with string.

2.   In an enormous stockpot, bring water, salt, lemon juice, cayenne and flavor sack to a bubble. Utilizing tongs add crab to stockpot; come back to a bubble. Decrease heat; stew, secured, until shells turn splendid red, around 15 minutes.

3.   Using tongs, expel crab from the pot. Dash under virus water or dive into ice water. Present with dissolved margarine and lemon wedges.

Foil-Packet Shrimp and Sausage Jambalaya

All out Time

Prep: 20 min. Heat: 20 min.

Makes

6 servings

1 parcel: 287 calories, 12g fat (4g immersed fat), 143mg cholesterol, 1068mg sodium, 23g starch (3g sugars, 2g fiber), 23g protein.

Ingredients

12 ounces completely cooked andouille wiener joins, cut into 1/2-inch cuts

12 ounces uncooked shrimp (31-40 for every pound), stripped and deveined

1 medium green pepper, slashed

1 medium onion, slashed

2 celery ribs, slashed

3 garlic cloves, minced

2 teaspoons Creole flavoring

1 can (14-1/2 ounces) fire-simmered diced tomatoes, depleted

1 cup uncooked moment rice

1 can (8 ounces) tomato sauce

1/2 cup chicken juices

Directions

1. Preheat broiler to 425°. In an enormous bowl, join all fixings. Partition blend among 6 lubed 18x12-in. Bits of substantial foil. Crease foil around blend and pleat edges to seal, framing bundles; place on a heating sheet. Prepare until shrimp turn pink and rice is delicate, 20-25 minutes.

Lemony Scallops with Angel Hair Pasta

Complete Time

Prep/Total Time: 25 min.

Makes

4   servings

Nourishment Facts: 1-1/2 cups: 404 calories, 13g fat (2g soaked fat), 27mg cholesterol, 737mg sodium, 48g starch (4g sugars, 6g fiber), and 25g protein.

Ingredients

8 ounces uncooked multigrain holy messenger hair pasta

3 tablespoons olive oil, separated

1 pound ocean scallops, tapped dry

2 cups cut radishes (around 1 pack)

2 garlic cloves, cut

1/2 teaspoon squashed red pepper chips 6 green onions, daintily cut 1/2 teaspoon legitimate salt

1 tablespoon ground lemon get-up-and-go 1/4 cup lemon juice

Directions

1.   In a 6-qt. stockpot, cook pasta as per bundle bearings; channel and come back to the pot.

2.   Meanwhile, in a huge skillet, heat 2 tablespoons oil over medium-high warmth; singe scallops in clusters until misty and edges are brilliant darker, around 2 minutes for every side. Expel from skillet; keep warm.

3.   In a similar skillet, saute radishes, garlic and pepper chips in residual oil until radishes are delicate, 2-3 minutes. Mix in green onions and salt; cook 1 moment. Add to pasta; hurl to consolidate. Sprinkle with lemon pizzazz and juice. Top with scallops to serve.

Pan-Seared Salmon with Dill Sauce

Complete Time

Prep/Total Time: 25 min.

Makes

4 servings

Nourishment Facts: 1 salmon filet with 1/4 cup sauce: 366 calories, 25g fat (4g soaked fat), 92mg cholesterol, 349mg sodium, 4g starch (3g sugars, 0 fibers), 31g protein. Diabetic trades: 4 lean meat, 2-1/2 fat.

Ingredients:

1 tablespoon canola oil

4 salmon filets (6 ounces each)

1 teaspoon Italian flavoring

1/4 teaspoon salt

1/2 cup decreased fat plain yogurt

1/4 cup decreased fat mayonnaise

1/4 cup finely hacked cucumber

1 teaspoon cut crisp dill

Directions

1.   In a huge skillet, heat oil over medium-high warmth. Sprinkle salmon with Italian flavoring and salt. A spot in skillet, skin side down. Lessen warmth to medium. Cook until fish just starts to drop effectively with a fork, around 5 minutes on each side.

2.   Meanwhile, in a little bowl, join yogurt, mayonnaise, cucumber, and dill. Present with salmon.

Chicken, Beef and Pork

Now let me give you some freestyle red beef and pork recipes. It might be tempting to write off meat in your diet, but for a fact, no single food is unhealthy. It is mostly about creating a healthy dietary pattern and applying moderations.

The fact is that red meats contain high levels of protein, which I'm sure you know helps to build the bones and muscles in our bodies. So, why should we avoid them when it can be of great benefit to our healthy living?

Also, chicken makes a fantastic weight loss-friendly staple, no doubt. Chicken breasts without skin or bone are rich in protein. You can bake, roast, or stuff a chicken dinner, and you can also serve in a soup or sandwich. You won't go wrong unless you keep to old boring recipes.

While everyone is guilty of sticking to common meal ideas, you don't have to eat the same kind of chicken twice as a king or queen that you are, the reason being that there are so many creative ways to combine the ingredients and serve up delicious flavor.

To help you set a chicken meal on your table today (and every other day), I have handpicked the most delicious chicken dishes, all of which I have personally taste-tested. You will spend less than 60 minutes cooking, making it possible to get in and out of the kitchen quickly and back to more important things.

Chicken Bruschetta

SmartPoints value: Green plan - 1SP, Blue plan - 1SP, Purple plan - 1SP

Total Time: 20 min, Prep time: 10 min, Cooking time: 10 min, Serves: 4

Nutritional value: Calories - 187, Carbs – 4.4g, Fat - 7g, Protein – 27.3g

When the weather is heating up, I mostly crave for fresh and light meals other than rich and comforting.

My most recently found new love when it comes to dessert is this deliciously prepared Italian Chicken Bruschetta. It's just so simple, simply made with fresh tomatoes, basil, and garlic. I've tried it several times, and one sweet thing about it is the refreshing flavors. There is just something about the way the fresh and juicy tomato works together with the bright basil and bold garlic.

While preparing, I like to add some grilled chicken breast to it as a lean protein. If you've noticed, I do more of chicken breast, yes, because it is low in points, and it's a perfect way of adding protein to my meal without getting over budget with my points.

Ingredients

Chicken breast (skinless, boneless) - 1 lb

Large Roma tomatoes (finely diced) - 2 pieces

Basil (finely chopped, fresh) - 1/4 cup

Garlic (minced) - 2 cloves

Olive oil (1 tbsp plus 1 tsp)

Balsamic Vinegar (1/2 tsp)

Parsley (dried) - 1 tsp

Oregano (dried) - 1 tsp

Pepper and Salt to taste

Instructions

1.   After cutting the chicken breasts into four equal-sized fillets, season each of the side of the chicken with the parsley, oregano and salt and pepper.

2.   Over medium-high heat, heat one teaspoon of olive oil in a medium-sized, nonstick skillet. For 4-5 minutes, cook as you turn each side until the chicken is entirely cooked and browned.

3.   Remove from heat and cover with a lid to allow it to sit for about 5 minutes.

4.   Make bruschetta by mixing tomatoes, olive oil, garlic, basil, balsamic vinegar, and pepper and salt in a bowl.

5.   Put the chicken breast on a plate and top each of them with about ¼ cup of the bruschetta. Then drizzle on some extra balsamic if you so desire.

6.   You can also make a sandwich with fresh Italian bread and little creamy goat cheese. The flavor is so bold and mouthwatering.

Lemon Chicken with Broccoli

SmartPoints value: Green plan - 3SP, Blue plan - 1SP, Purple plan - 1SP

Total Time: 30 min, Prep time: 15 min, Cooking time: 15 min, Serves: 4

Nutritional value:

Calories - 176.6, Carbs - 8.4g, Fat - 2.0g, Protein - 32.3g

The whole family will love this fantastic weeknight dinner, and it's ready in just 30 minutes. To ensure that the chicken cooks quickly and evenly, you should slice it thinly. Cover the pan when cooking the broccoli to help build up steam, bathing the florets with heat. It will allow tops that aren't in contact with the hot pan to cook properly. You will need one small to medium head of broccoli to get enough florets and one lemon to yield enough zest and juice for this entrée.

Ingredients

All-purpose flour - 2 Tbsp

Black pepper - ¼ tsp (freshly ground)

Fat-free, reduced-sodium chicken broth - 1½ cup(s) (divided)

Fresh lemon juice - 1 Tbsp

Fresh parsley - 2 Tbsp (chopped)

Lemon zest - 2 tsp, or more to taste*

Minced Garlic - 2 tsp

Olive oil - 2 tsp

Table salt - ½ tsp (divided)

Uncooked chicken breast(s) -12 oz, thinly sliced (boneless, skinless)

Uncooked broccoli - 2½ cup(s), small florets

Instructions

1.   On a clean plate, mix 1 1/2 Tbsp of flour, 1/4 tsp of salt, and pepper, then add chicken and turn to coat.

2.   Put a large nonstick skillet over medium-high heat and pour the oil in for heating.

3.   Add the chicken and cook, turning as needed, until it is lightly browned and cooked through, about 5 minutes; remove to a plate.

4.   Put one cup of broth and Garlic in the same skillet, then boil over high heat, scraping up browned bits from the bottom of the pan with a wooden spoon.

5.   Add the broccoli, then cover and cook for 1 minute.

6.   Stir the remaining 1/2 cup broth, 1/2 Tbsp flour, and 1/4 tsp salt together in a small cup, then add to the skillet and bring its content to a simmer over low heat.

7.   Cover the skillet and cook until the broccoli is crisp-tender and the sauce thickens slightly.

8.   Stir in the chicken and lemon zest, then heat through.

9.   Remove the skillet from heat, and stir in the parsley and lemon juice, then toss to coat.

Chicken and Fennel in Rosemary-wine Broth

SmartPoints value: Green plan - 4SP, Blue plan - 2SP, Purple plan - 2SP

Total Time: 40 min, Prep time: 18 min, Cooking time: 22 min, Serves: 4

Nutritional value: Calories - 121.5, Carbs - 10.5g, Fat - **6.3g**, Protein - 26.0g

If you are looking for a dish that will tickle your belly on a chilly night, this rustic Italian entrée is perfect, and since you will cook it in one skillet, that makes it easy to fix in your vegetable. You should first sear the chicken to produce an excellent brown exterior. You can then sauté the fennel and onion in the flavorful drippings left in the skillet. They will mix and become sweetened as they cook.

Return the chicken and any accumulated juices to the skillet to finish cooking.

Ingredients

All-purpose flour - 5 tsp (divided)

Black pepper - ⅛ tsp, or to taste (freshly ground)

Canned chicken broth - 14½ oz

Minced Garlic - 2 tsp

Olive oil - 1 Tbsp, extra-virgin (divided)

Red/white wine - 1/4 cup

Rosemary - 1¼ tsp, fresh (chopped)

Table salt - ½ tsp, or to taste

Uncooked chicken breast(s) - 1 pound(s), cut into bite-size chunks (boneless, skinless)

Uncooked fennel bulb(s) - 1 pound(s)

Uncooked red onion(s) - 1 small (chopped)

Instructions

1. Trim the stalk from fennel to quarter bulb(s) lengthwise and then slice in a cross-like manner into small pieces. Reserve the fronds for garnish (about 3 cups fennel will be available).

2. Put the chicken on a plate and sprinkle it with rosemary, then sprinkle it with 4 tsp flour and toss to coat.

3. Add 1 tsp of oil to a large nonstick skillet and heat over medium-high heat.

4. Add the chicken and cook, occasionally turning with tongs, until it is lightly brown.

5. Transfer the chicken to a clean plate (cooking is partial at this point).

6. Heat the remaining 2 tsp oil in the same skillet over medium-high heat and add fennel and onion; sauté until it becomes lightly brown and almost tender.

7. Add wine and Garlic, then reduce the heat to low and simmer, stirring the bottom of the pan to scrape up browned bits, until most of the wine has evaporated.

8. Stir the broth together with the remaining 1 tsp flour in a small bowl and then stir into skillet.

9. Add salt and pepper, then increase the heat to high and bring it to a boil. Reduce the heat to medium-low and simmer for another 1 minute.

10.   Add the chicken and cook, often tossing until the chicken cooks through. Garnish with reserved chopped fennel fronds and serve.

You can serve it with crusty whole-grain bread, or over rice, to mop up all of the broth.

If you prefer not to use wine in this recipe, you can substitute with one tablespoon of red or white wine vinegar and three tablespoons of water.

Chicken Cordon Bleu

SmartPoints value: Green plan - 6SP, Blue plan - 4SP, Purple plan - 4SP

Total Time: 46 min, Prep time: 11 min, Cooking time: 35 min, Serves: 4

Nutritional value: Calories - 357.9, Carbs - 12.7g, Fat - 16.9g, Protein - 36.7g

Cordon bleu was a commonly served dish at dinner-parties in the sixties. Preparing it is simple: You sandwich a layer of ham and cheese between thin medallions of chicken or veal, then you sauté it.

Here, I have created a light version of the recipe to use a single layer of chicken rolled around the filling to make an elegant presentation.

Prepare this dish the next time you have guests and add some greens to the plate: either roasted broccolini, asparagus, or haricot vert (thin French green beans) will do just fine.

Ingredients

All-purpose flour - 4 Tbsp

Black pepper - ⅛ tsp (or to taste), freshly ground

Cornflake crumbs - ½ cup(s)

Lean ham (cooked) - 4 slice(s), (about 2 oz. total)

Egg(s) - 1 large, lightly beaten

Ground nutmeg - ⅛ tsp

Parmesan cheese - 2 Tbsp, freshly grated

Reduced-sodium chicken broth - ½ cup(s)

Swiss cheese - 2 oz (4 thin slices), low-fat

Table salt - ½ tsp

Table wine - 1 Tbsp, Madeira

Uncooked chicken breast(s) -1 pound(s), (4 breasts, 1/4 pound each), pounded to ¼-inch thickness (boneless, skinless)

2% reduced-fat milk - ½ cup(s)

Instructions

1.   Spray a baking sheet with nonstick spray while you preheat the oven to 400°F.

2.   Place one half of a chicken breast on a work surface and top it with one slice of the ham, then one slice of the Swiss cheese.

3.   Roll it up in a jelly-roll style, and secure with a toothpick. Repeat the process with the remaining chicken, ham, and cheese.

4.   Make a mixture of two tablespoons of flour, one-quarter teaspoon of salt, and ground pepper on a sheet of wax paper.

5.   Place the egg and the cornflake crumbs in separate shallow bowls.

6.   Taking it one at a time, coat the chicken rolls lightly, first with the flour mixture, and then dip it into the egg for a single layer coat.

7.   Coat the rolls with the cornflake crumbs, and place them on the baking sheet (discard any leftover flour mixture, egg, and cornflake bits).

8.   Spray the chicken rolls lightly with nonstick spray. Bake until the temperature of the rolls reaches 160°F, 30–35 minutes.

9.   To prepare the sauce, mix the milk, the broth, the Madeira, nutmeg, the remaining two tablespoons of flour, the remaining 1/4 teaspoon of salt, and another grinding of the pepper in a medium-sized saucepan.

10.   Whisk until it is smooth and cook over medium heat, continually whisking until it becomes thick in about 6 minutes.

11.   Remove the sauce from the heat and stir in the Parmesan cheese, then cover to keep it warm.

12.   When the chicken rolls are ready, drizzle them with the sauce and serve them immediately.

Peanut Butter Sandwich Snacks

SmartPoints value: Green plan - 3SP, Blue plan - 3SP, Purple plan - 3SP
Total Time: 5 min, Prep time: 5 min, Serves: 1
Nutritional value: Calories - 327, Carbs - 30g, Fat - 17.9g, Protein - 15.0g

When you're looking for something sweet, chocolaty, and rich in nutrients, this easy-to-make snack will do the job. I make use of chocolate syrup as an alternative to melted chocolate. I observed that chocolate syrup has fewer Smart Points, and the small amount spreads farther. I should let you know that the chocolate syrup will not get hard, even when you refrigerate.

Ingredients

Peanut butter (powdered) - 1 Tbsp

Water - 2¼ tsp

Crispbread, Whole Grain (34 degrees) - 6 crackers, or similar product

Chocolate syrup - 1½ tsp

Sprinkles - ¼ tsp, nonpareil

Instructions

1.   Mix the powdered peanut butter and water in a clean small bowl and stir until it becomes smooth.

2.   Spread the peanut butter evenly over three crackers and top it with the remaining three crackers biscuit or bread.

3.   Take half a teaspoon of chocolate syrup and spread it over half the top of each cracker sandwich — top chocolate syrup with sprinkles.

Peanut Butter Apple Slices

SmartPoints value: Green plan - 4SP, Blue plan - 4SP, Purple plan - 4SP

Total time: 10 min, Prep time: 10 min, Serves: 4

Nutritional value: Calories - 218, Carbs – 31.3g, Fat – 8.1g, Protein – 11.6g

Having a healthy snack ready in about 10 minutes is a thing of joy for me. Peanut butter apple slices are just what fits into the picture of a healthy quick, nutritious snack. This apple slice is a simple and easy meal rich in protein and fiber. It is topped with peanut butter and decorated with chocolate chips and slivered almonds.

Ingredients

Large apples - 2 pieces

Powdered peanut butter (reconstituted) - 1/2 cup

Semi-sweet chocolate chips - 2 tbsp

Slivered almonds - 2 tbsp

Pecans (chopped) - 2 tbsp

Instructions

1.   Remove the core of the apple using a small paring knife or an apple corer

2.   Slice the apples into thick rings.

3.   Add the peanut butter on the apple slices.

4.   Use chips and nuts for top-up

Baked Plantains

SmartPoints value: Green plan - 5SP, Blue plan - 5SP, Purple plan - 5SP
Total time: 40 min, Prep time: 5 min, Cooking time: 35min, Serves: 2
Nutritional value: Calories - 184, Carbs - 47g, Fat – 0.5g, Protein - 2g

Baked plantain is just as healthy as it is tasty. The plantain is full of good for your ingredients.

Ingredients

Very overripe plantains (2 medium-sized)

Misting spray (Olive oil)

Salt to taste

Instructions

1. On a preheated oven of 350 degrees, line a baking sheet with a silicone mat or parchment paper and spray with olive oil or non-fat cooking spray.

2. Thinly slice plantains and place them on the baking sheet evenly, then lightly mist with olive oil or the non-fat cooking spray and sprinkle with a bit of salt.

3. For about 30-35 minutes, cook in the oven flipping once about halfway through until they become golden and mostly crisp.

Baked plantains are easy to prepare and very firm. They taste sweeter when overly ripe, and firmer when they are not as ripe. Feel free to choose your style of plantain.

Strawberries & Cream Chocolate Cookie Sandwich

SmartPoints value: Green plan - 3SP, Blue plan - 3SP, Purple plan - 3SP

Total time: 5 min, Prep time: 5 min, Serves: 1

Nutritional value: Calories - 280, Carbs - 37g, Fat - 12g, Protein - 5g

I'm sure you will love this tasty summer treat. This chocolate cookie sandwich will remind you of your favorite childhood ice cream sandwich. This version is healthier, upgraded, and way easier to make in your kitchen! You can impress your loved ones with this delicious dessert/snack by making dozens of them for parties, barbecues, or special occasions with family and friends. If you don't have strawberries, you can substitute with any ripe fruit you have on hand like peaches, bananas, or raspberries.

Ingredients

Topping (lite whipped) - 2 Tbsp Strawberries (hulled, sliced) - 1 medium

Graham cracker(s) (chocolate variety) - 2 square(s)

Instructions

1.   Scoop whipped topping onto one square-shaped graham cracker.

2.   Top it with sliced strawberries and place another cracker on top of that.

Mini chocolate chip cookies

SmartPoints value: Green plan - 1SP, Blue plan - 1SP, Purple plan - 1SP

Total time: 26 min, Prep time: 10 min, Cooking time: 6 min, Serves: 48

Nutritional value: Calories - 113.7, Carbs - 16.4g, Fat - 5.9g, Protein - 0.6g

These bite-size cookies might be small, but they pack a chocolate punch. I often use dark brown sugar in making these cookies as it contains more molasses than the light brown variety. The dark brown sugar adds a rich, complex flavor to these cookies, making them moist and chewy. In case you have only light brown sugar available, you don't have to go out of your way to get the dark variety. That will work just fine. You can replace the chocolate chips with any other one you like, be it cinnamon chips, toffee, butterscotch, or white chocolate chips. You can even stir in some chopped nuts to make things a little cDashchy.

Ingredients

Butter (salted, softened) - 2 Tbsp

Canola oil - 2 tsp

Brown sugar (packed, dark-variety) - ½ cup(s)

Vanilla extract - 1 tsp

Table salt - ⅛ tsp

Egg white(s) - 1 large

All-purpose flour - ¾ cup(s)

Baking soda - ¼ tsp

Chocolate chips (semi-sweet) - 3 oz, about 1/2 cup

Instructions

1.	Prepare the oven by preheating it to 375°F.

2.	Mix the butter, oil, and sugar in a medium bowl.

3.	Add vanilla and egg white, then mix thoroughly to combine. Toss in some salt to taste.

4.	Mix the flour and baking soda in a small bowl and stir them into the batter.

5.	Add the chocolate chips to the batter and stir to distribute evenly throughout.

6.	Put forty-eight half-teaspoons of dough onto two large nonstick baking sheets. Leave small spaces between the cookies.

7.	Bake the cookies until they become golden around the edges; about 4 to 6 minutes.

8.	Cool the baked cookies on a wire rack.

Chocolate-Peppermint Thins

SmartPoints value: Green plan - 3SP, Blue plan - 3SP, Purple plan   -   3SP
Total Time: 1hr 16 min, Prep time: 15 min, Cooking time: 5 min, Serves: 16
Nutritional value: Calories - 175, Carbs – 21g, Fat – 5g, Protein – 7g
My homemade chocolate peppermint thin comes with a splash of peppermint extract, and divine copycat thin mint cookies to satisfy my cravings

Ingredients

Chocolate chunk (coarsely chopped) - 3½ oz

Chocolate wafer(s) (thin variety) - 16 item(s)

Candy cane (finely crushed) - 1 oz

Instructions

1.   Arrange a large baking sheet with parchment or paper wax and line cookies close together in a single layer.

2.   At 5 seconds interval, melt chocolate in a microwavable bowl and stir between each interval until all but one or two pieces melted, then remove from microwave and stir until fully dissolved.

3.   Put the melted chocolate in a plastic bag and cut off a corner; in a zig-zag pattern, pipe the chocolate over cookies and sprinkle with the crushed candy cane, keep it refrigerated until its set for at least an hour or overnight. Serve as desired (1 cookie per serving)

Chocolate-Dipped Baby Bananas

SmartPoints value: Green plan - 3SP, Blue plan - 3SP, Purple plan   -   3SP
Total time: 20 min, Prep time: 5 min, Cooking time: --, Serves: 12
Nutritional value: Calories - 210, Carbs – 31.2g, Fat – 1g, Protein –   5.4g
Chocolate-dipped baby bananas are just perfect for casual parties for both kids and adults. With the banana and chocolate combination, it's so irresistible. Alternatively, you can replace baby bananas with four regular bananas cut crosswise into thirds.

Ingredients

Baby-variety banana (peeled) - 12 small

Chocolate (semisweet, chopped) - 3 oz

Butter (unsalted) - ¾ tsp

Coconut (shredded, unsweetened) - 2 tbsp

Instructions

1.   Place large baking sheet with wax paper and insert wooden craft stick in one end of each banana.

2.   Mix butter and chocolate in a medium microwave bowl, then microwave on high heat for about 1minute.

3.   Taking one banana after another spoon the chocolate over the bananas cover, and sprinkle it with coconut while it is on a baking sheet. Keep it refrigerated until the chocolate sets in about 15 minutes.

4.   Serve as desired (1 banana per serving)

Smoothies and Drinks Recipes

It is funny that most people don't consider water to be a drink. When you talk about drinks, everyone is thinking of everything else except the best one of all.

Drinking two cups (one pint) of water right before food helps weight watchers to lose some extra pounds according to research.

Those two cups of water will not only help you with your weight loss goals, but they can also boost your mood, improve your metabolism, increase your brainpower, and help you deal with stress better. Shreds of evidence from science suggest that hydration gives a plethora of health benefits, and the fact is, when it comes to having an understanding of all of the roles that water plays in our body, scientists have just scratched the surface.

Mango Salsa

SmartPoints value: Green plan - 0SP, Blue plan - 0SP, Purple plan - 0SP

Total time: 15 min, Prep time: 15 min, Cooking time: 0 min, Serves: 4

Nutritional value: Calories – 71, Carbs – 17.7g, Fat – 0.5g, Protein – 1.3g

The mango salsa is a great snack full of fruits and veggies. Although salsa goes well with chips, it doesn't mean that you can use it for other things. However, it's an excellent topper for fish, chicken, and even salads.

Ingredients

Large mango (peeled and diced) - 1 item

Red onion (finely chopped) - 1/2

Red bell pepper (chopped) - 1 cup

Jalapeno pepper (seeded and chopped) - (1 small piece)

Garlic (minced) - 2 cloves

Lime juice - 1 cup

Pinch of salt (add to taste)

Instructions

1.   Put all the ingredients in a bowl and season as desired with salt.

2.   This mouthwatering sweet and savory salsa awakens your taste buds with delicious flavors. It is fresh, light, and loaded with antioxidants that make it a great pair with tortilla chips.

Watermelon Aguas Frescas

SmartPoints value: 3SP
Total time: 5 min, Prep time: 5 min, Serves – 4
Nutritional value: Calories - 57, Carbs - 14g, Fat - 0g, Protein - 1g
This pure Mexican blend of watermelon, lime juice, water, and a little sugar produces a delightful means of quenching thirst for Weight Watchers on a summer afternoon. You can find an alternative for the cantaloupe if you like.

Ingredients

Watermelon (seedless, ripe; make sure it's nice and sweet) - 4 cups cubed

Sugar (honey or agave nectar as an alternative) - 1 tbsp (or to taste)

Water - 3 cups

Lime juice (fresh) - 2-3 tsps.

Mint (fresh) for garnish, if you desire

Instructions

1.   Put the cubed watermelon in a blender and add 1-1/2 cups of the water, the lime juice, and the sugar. Blend everything at high speed until smooth.

2.   Sieve the liquid blend through a medium strainer into a large pitcher (or bowl).

3.   Pour in the remaining 1-1/2 cups of water and stir.

4.   Chill in a refrigerator for 1 hour or longer, depending on the temperature you like.

5.   Drop a few cubes of ice in a glass and pour in the watermelon agua fresca.

6.   Add a mint sprig to garnish if you desire.

Chocolate Peanut Butter Banana Protein Shake

SmartPoints value: 6SP

Total time: 5 min, Prep time: 5 min, Serves: 1

Nutritional value: Calories - 299, Carbs - 29.6g, Fat - 6.1g, Protein - 36.2g

This drink provides a fast, healthy, and delicious way to begin your day, packed with protein to help keep you satisfied until lunchtime.

Ingredients

Cottage cheese (non-fat) - 1/2 cup

Peanut Butter Flour (PB2) - 2 tablespoons

Chocolate protein powder - 1 scoop

Banana (frozen) - 1/2 finger

A handful of ice cubes

Sweetener - to taste (You may not need this if your protein powder already has sweetener in it)

Instructions

1.   Mix all the ingredients in a blender and process until you get a smooth mixture.

2.   You can add more ice cubes to give a thicker consistency to the protein shake.

3.   You can use less ice if you want your drink to be thinner. Add more water.

Skinny Pina Colada

SmartPoints - 7SP

Total time: 5 min, Prep time: 5 min, Serves: 1

Nutritional value: Calories - 183, Carbs - 11g, Fat - 0.5g, Protein - 9.5g

This drink recipe is a cleaned-up version of a pina colada from the Weight Watchers, thickened with vanilla protein powder instead of the cream of coconut. This satisfying and sweet drink has just 7 SmartPoints, which is about 1/3 of the points of a traditional Pina Colada.

Ingredients

Vanilla protein powder with about 100 calories per 1-ounce serving (natural) - 3 tablespoons

Crushed pineapple packed in juice (canned, not drained) - 1/4 cup

White rum - 1 -1/2 ounces

Coconut extract - 1/8 teaspoon

Crushed ice, about eight ice cubes - 1 cup

Instructions

1.   Put all the ingredients in a blender.

2.   Pour in half a cup of water, and blend at high speed until it is smooth.

Spindrift Grapefruit

SmartPoints value: 1SP

Serving size - 355ml

Nutritional value: Calories - 17, Carbs - 4g, Fat - 0g, Protein - 0g

Spindrift is America's first sparkling water fruit drink.

The several varieties of the drink are all created from sparkling water and real squeezed fruits.

Aside from the grapefruit variety, the other types you can enjoy with your meal include blackberry, cucumber, lemon, raspberry lime, orange mango, strawberry, half & half, and cranberry raspberry.

Ingredients

The ingredients of Grapefruit drink include grapefruit juice, lemon juice, orange juice.

Vegan Snake Recipes

It is mid-morning, and you're feeling a little peckish - what will you eat? You feel a bit deprived because you are on the vegan diet, and you can't think of any tasty and quick snack ideas. Or perhaps you've just come home from work and are craving a yummy treat, but you are tired. You, therefore, want your vegan food to be easy, hassle-free, and not one of the most complicated time-consuming recipes on the planet, even better - preferably just something that you can throw together in under 5 or 10 minutes.

Below is a list of some tasty, fast, and easy vegan food and snack recipe ideas to help make your life a little easier.

Popcorn

It's a tasty, rather low-calorie snack that can be ready to eat in under 10 minutes. It's perfect if you're craving something a little salty.

Nutritional Facts

servings per container	5
Prep Total	**10 min**
Serving Size	8
Amount per serving **Calories**	**0%**
	% Daily Value
Total Fat 3g	**20%**
Saturated Fat 4g	32%
Trans Fat 2g	2%
Cholesterol	**2%**
Sodium 110mg	**0.2%**
Total Carbohydrate 21g	**50%**
Dietary Fiber 9g	1%
Total Sugar 1g	1%
Protein 1g	
Vitamin C 7mcg	17%
Calcium 60mg	1%
Iron 7mg	10%
Potassium 23mg	21%

Ingredient & Process

Place 2 tablespoons of olive oil and ¼ Cup popcorn in a large saucepan.

Cover with a lid, and cook the popcorn over a medium flame, ensuring that you are shaking constantly. Just when you think that it's not working, keep on enduring for another minute or two, and the popping will begin.

When the popping stops, take off from the heat and place in a large bowl.

Add plenty of salt to taste, and if desired, dribble in ¼ Cup to ½ Cup of melted coconut oil. If you are craving sweet popcorn, add some maple syrup to the coconut oil, about ½ Cup, or to taste.

5 Minutes or Less Vegan Snacks

Here's a list of basically 'no-preparation required' vegan snack ideas that you can munch on anytime:

Nutritional Facts

servings per container	5
Prep Total	**10 min**
Serving Size	8
Amount per serving **Calories**	**0%**
	% Daily Value
Total Fat 20g	**190%**
Saturated Fat 2g	32%
Trans Fat 1g	2%
Cholesterol	**2%**
Sodium 70mg	**0.2%**
Total Carbohydrate 32g	**150%**
Dietary Fiber 8g	1%
Total Sugar 1g	1%
Protein 3g	
Vitamin C 7mcg	17%
Calcium 210mg	1%
Iron 4mg	10%
Potassium 25mg	20%

Ingredients and Process

Trail mix: nuts, dried fruit, and vegan chocolate pieces.

Fruit pieces with almond butter, peanut butter or vegan chocolate spread

Frozen vegan cake, muffin, brownie or slice that you made on the weekend

Vegetable sticks (carrots, celery, and cucumber etc.) with a Vegan Dip (homemade or store-bought) such as hummus or beetroot dip. (Careful of the store-bought ingredients though).

Smoothie - throw into the blender anything you can find (within limits!) such as soy milk, coconut milk, rice milk, almond milk, soy yogurt, coconut milk yogurt, cinnamon, spices, sea salt, berries, bananas, cacao powder, vegan chocolate, agave nectar, maple syrup, chia seeds, flax seeds, nuts, raisins, sultanas... What you put into your smoothie is up to you, and you can throw it all together in less than 5 minutes!

Crackers with avocado, soy butter, and tomato slices, or hummus spread.

Packet chips (don't eat them too often). There are many vegan chip companies that make kale chips, corn chips, potato chips, and vegetable chips, so enjoy a small bowl now and again.

Fresh Fruit

The health benefits of eating fresh fruit daily should not be minimized. So, make sure that you enjoy some in-season fruit as one of your daily vegan snacks.

Nutritional Facts

servings per container	10
Prep Total	**10 min**
Serving Size	5/5
Amount per serving **Calories**	**1%**
	% Daily Value
Total Fat 24g	**2%**
Saturated Fat 8g	3%
Trans Fat 4g	2%
Cholesterol	**2%**
Sodium 10mg	**22%**
Total Carbohydrate 7g	**54%**
Dietary Fiber 4g	1%
Total Sugar 1g	1%
Protein 1g	24
Vitamin C 2mcg	17%
Calcium 270mg	15%
Iron 17mg	20%
Potassium 130mg	2%

Ingredients:

Chop your favorite fruit and make a fast and easy fruit salad, adding some squeezed orange juice to make a nice juicy dressing.

Serve with some soy or coconut milk yogurt or vegan ice-cream if desired, and top with some tasty walnuts or toasted slithered almonds to make it a sustaining snack.

Vegan Brownie

Nutritional Facts

servings per container	3
Prep Total	**10 min**
Serving Size	7
Amount per serving **Calories**	**20%**
	% Daily Value
Total Fat 3g	**22%**
Saturated Fat 22g	8%
Trans Fat 17g	21%
Cholesterol	**20%**
Sodium 120mg	**70%**
Total Carbohydrate 30g	**57%**
Dietary Fiber 4g	8%
Total Sugar 10g	8%
Protein 6g	
Vitamin C 1mcg	1%
Calcium 20mg	31%
Iron 2mg	12%
Potassium 140mg	92%

Ingredients:

1/2 cup non-dairy butter melted

5 tablespoons cocoa

1 cup granulated sugar

3 teaspoons Ener-G egg replacer

1/4 cup water

1 teaspoon vanilla

3/4 cup flour

1 teaspoon baking powder

1/2 teaspoon salt

1/2 cup walnuts (optional)

Instructions:

1. Heat oven to 350º. Prepare an 8" x 8" baking pan with butter or canola oil.

2. Combine butter, cocoa, and sugar in a large bowl.

3. Mix the egg replacer and water in a blender until frothy.

4. Add to the butter mixture with vanilla. Add the flour, baking powder, and salt, and mix thoroughly.

5. Add the walnuts if desired. Pour the batter into the pan, and spread evenly.

6. Bake for 40 to 45 minutes, or until a toothpick inserted comes out clean.

Lightning Source UK Ltd.
Milton Keynes UK
UKHW021856220421
382471UK00003B/251